PEACE, BE STILL

HYMNS OF SUSAN PALO CHERWIEN

VOLUME THREE

AUGSBURG FORTRESS

Peace, Be Still
Hymns of Susan Palo Cherwien, Volume Three
Susan Palo Cherwien

Editor: Robert Buckley Farlee
Cover art: Copyright © iStock/Thinkstock
Cover design: Laurie Ingram

The paper used in this publication meets the minimum requirements of American National Standard for Information Sciences—Permanence of Paper for Printed Materials, ANSI Z329.48-1984.
Printed in the USA.

ISBN 978-1-5064-2222-0

To David,
who has brought such
glorious music to my
life and to the voice
of the church

Spirit of God, resound in us
With songs of beauty, hymns of life,
That beauty from our voices rise
In echoed tones melodious;
Alleluia.

PUBLISHER'S NOTE

Because finely crafted hymn texts have a poetic imagery of their own, Susan Palo Cherwien's hymns appear in text form in the first section of this volume. To enable their use by congregations, the hymns are also presented with music, beginning on page 57.

In addition to several widely used tunes, a number of new tunes by several noted composers are included in this collection. Some of these were commissioned, along with the texts, for particular occasions; in other cases the author wrote a text with a particular tune in mind; in still other cases, where no suitable existing tune could be found, a composer was invited to contribute a new tune. These are not intended to be exclusive pairings, however. Composers are invited to let these hymn texts inspire other melodies and musical settings for assembly, soloist, or choir.

See also Susan Palo Cherwien's previous collections of hymns, both books published by Augsburg Fortress:

- *O Blessed Spring*
- *Come, Beloved of the Maker*

CONTENTS

HYMNS

ABIDE IN US, O BREAD OF LIFE

Abide in us, O Bread of Life,
That we abide in You,
And we in taking bread partake
Of all that is in You.

True food infuse our very flesh;
True drink our days revive,
As in Yourself we find ourselves
And You in us give life.

Now for the journey strengthen us;
Your Heart in us increase,
That here Your Spirit may abide
And make each day a feast.

So change us by this holy grace,
This gift of love outpoured,
That we become Your bread on earth
And live for all the world.

ALL-EMBRACING GOD

All-embracing God,
Builder of all worlds,
In your house your people rise to praise;
By your Holy Name
Signed and marked and sealed,
May our hearts become your dwelling place.

All-embracing Christ,
Servant of all worlds,
Humbly seeking out the last and least,
By your Holy Love
Signed and marked and sealed,
May we strive for justice and for peace.

All-embracing Fire,
Spirit of all worlds,
Prodding all God's people to evolve,
By your Holy Gifts
Signed and marked and sealed,
May we seek and serve all that you love.

All-embracing church,
Gathered from all worlds,
Temple of the Fire, the Love, the Name,
By the font and meal
Signed and marked and sealed,
May we in fair lives God's grace proclaim.

All-embracing God,
Trinity of Love,
Dwell within us now, do not delay;
Make your church alive
With your very life
In the Now that does not pass away.

AS YOUR SPIRIT IN THE DESERT

Cantor or choir   As your Spirit in the desert
Led the Christ to dust and stone,
So instill our hearts with courage
Now to cross where Christ has gone.

Assembly   Let us cross into the wilderness
So to walk where Christ has gone.

Cantor or choir   As your fire and cloudy pillar
Israel's tribes to Canaan led,
May your presence be our comfort,
May your manna be our bread.

Assembly   Let us cross into the wilderness
With God's manna as our bread.

Cantor or choir   Though wild beasts may lurk in shadow,
And dire thirst may sear and sting,
You have promised living waters
Waiting for us at the spring.

Assembly   Let us cross out of the wilderness
To the waters of the spring.

Cantor or choir   Through the narrow gate now draw us,
Past all empire's pull and strife,
Where beyond our fear and clinging
Stands the threshold of new life.

Assembly   Let us cross out of the wilderness
To the threshold of new life.

Cantor or choir   God of Desert, God of Promise,
You have bid us journey on
Through the days of dust and darkness
To the rising of the dawn.

Assembly   Let us cross out of the wilderness
To the rising of the dawn.

BEHOLD THE LILIES OF THE FIELD

Behold the lilies of the field,
Berobed in raiment fair:
They do not loom or spindle wield,
Yet bloom without a care.

Behold the singing birds of air,
Aloft in joyful flight:
Upheld by God's unflagging care,
They soar in God's delight.

Why, then, by cares and dread consumed?
Why so cast down, distressed?
If God so cares for bird and bloom,
Will God regard you less?

O hope in God, the living God,
In whom all live and move;
Each precious day be met with awe;
Each precious face, with love.

So let the morrow's sun arise;
With joy its light caress,
For God, all-loving, caring, wise,
Will comfort and will bless.

BEYOND THE MIND'S IMAGINING

Beyond the mind's imagining,
Beyond the heart's desire,
The power of God to love and bless,
To prosper and inspire,
Be here among us nurturing
Our hearts with holy fire.

Enheartened by Christ's selfless life,
May we Christ's love enshrine,
And gathered in Christ's holy name
Unfold to the Divine,
By sacred story, holy song,
Sweet water and sweet wine.

Emboldened by the Spirit's gifts,
Afire with God's own grace,
May we true love and wisdom learn
Within God's warm embrace,
And thus true faithful servants prove
Through every time and place.

Where stone on stone our lives shall build,
Though storm or sun shall pass,
May every generation praise,
May God's great name be blessed.
That first and most within each heart
God's love may dwell at last.

BLESSED ONE, PARAGON

Refrain
Blessed One,
Paragon,
Holy gate and holy throne,
Bearer of the Midnight Son,
    O Holy Mother.

God invites,
You requite,
Vessel of the promised Light,
Shining into earthly night,
    O radiant Mother.   *Refrain*

At your vow,
Gabriel bows,
Cloister of the burgeoning bough,
Compassing the Christ about,
    O loving Mother.   *Refrain*

In your womb,
God finds room,
Burning bush of brightest bloom,
Flaming out, yet not consumed,
    O wondrous Mother.   *Refrain*

By your word,
For the world,
Temple of the living Word,
Bearing also sorrow's sword,
    O valiant Mother.   *Refrain*

Hope finds rest
At your breast,
Haven of the heavenly Guest,
Sheltering the infant blest,
    O gentle Mother.   *Refrain*

COME, O SPIRIT, COME TO US

VENI SANCTE SPIRITUS

Come, O Spirit, come to us,
Sending forth the luminous
Radiance of your holy light.

Come, O Parent of the Poor,
Come, O generous Treasure-store,
Come, O heart-illuming Light.

O most gracious Comforter,
Sweet and welcome Visitor,
Sweet and soothing Healing Light.

In our labor, be our rest,
In our temper, temperance,
In our tears, consoling sigh.

O most blessèd Light of God,
In our hearts make your abode,
Filling us with faith and sight.

Lest your will in us abide,
Nothing does in us reside,
Nothing that is whole and right.

Cleanse all that is soiled, impure,
Quench all that is dry and sere,
Cure all that is mortified.

Gentle what is stone in us,
Kindle what is ice in us,
Bridle what is lost and wild.

Grant this to your faithful host,
All who place in you their trust:
Sevenfold gifts in us ignite.

Grant the merit of the just,
Grant your sure deliverance,
Grant perpetual delight.

MEDIEVAL SEQUENCE
TR. © 2013 SUSAN PALO CHERWIEN, ADMIN. AUGSBURG FORTRESS

GOD HAS TOLD US, GOD HAS TAUGHT US

God has told us, God has taught us:
"I am present; do not fear."
God upholds this loving promise:
"I am present, ever near."
  Look, behold, receive, believe;
  Love and trust in God and live.

Christ has shown us, Christ has taught us:
"I am with you age to age."
As the vine is to the branches,
Love sustains us all our days.
  Nothing parts us, nor divides,
  From the love of God in Christ.

God has shown us, Christ has taught us:
"Know, Beloved, what is good":
Doing justice, loving kindness,
Walking humbly with your God,
  Prodded by the Spirit's fire,
  Living out God's deep desire.

Therefore, sisters, brothers, gladly
May we love and trust in God,
May we be as Christ's one body,
May we live the Spirit's good,
  That our hearts be God's fair home,
  'Til the reign of God shall come.

GOD, WHO SET THE SPHERES IN MOTION

God, who set the spheres in motion,
Times and seasons, dusk and dawn,
Ebb and tide of stream and ocean,
Turn and dance of star and sun,
All the turning of creation
Pulses from Your heart sublime;
Everything, it has its season,
Every purpose has its time.

Thus when days and lives are paling,
Death draws near us to embrace,
May our peaceful hearts unfailing
Trust in Your unchanging grace.
As the winter turns at solstice,
As the night turns toward the day,
All Your blessed seasons show us:
Life is changed, not swept away.

God, You bless us with companions,
Sisters, brothers, in this place;
We have sung them to Your mansions
Where they dwell in Your embrace.
Life in Christ leaves holy pathways;
Saintly signs lead us to see
As their blessèd lives bear witness:
All streams run into the sea.

Thus through all the times and seasons
To Your Name we lift our praise;
Even at the grave we sing it:
Alleluia, all our days.
Alleluia, for the newness
Hidden under twilight's gray;
Alleluia, for the promise:
Life is changed, not swept away.

GREAT GOD, WHOSE STORY

Great God, whose story age to age
Is sung by prophet, poet, sage,
Creation's web, spun with your hands
And casting into myriad strands,
Tells out your love in time and space,
A storied tapestry of grace.

In depths of earth you wove each frame
And called each precious one by name;
Now in your holy courts we view
How all your works are joined in you—
A threefold cord, not light undone:
Self, Neighbor, God, entwined in one.

The hymns of saints of yesterdays
Still sound when we our voices raise;
And generations yet to be
Take hope in every litany;
For through the Word, God new creates,
The past and future, interlaced.

By song, by sign, by word, by meal
Your loving presence is revealed;
Oh, may our stories join as one,
Creator, Christ, and Spirit, One,
That we may weave through endless days
A storied tapestry of grace.

HOLY WOMAN, GRACEFUL GIVER
(MARK 14)

Holy woman, graceful giver,
Prophet, servant, and believer,
Woman with the ointment jar,
Rose up near the time appointed
Broke the seal, Christ's head anointed
For the coming fatal hour.

Like the vessel, we are broken;
Like the ointment, we are token
Of God's loving unto death;
Like the woman, we are serving;
Like the scolders, ill deserving
Such a rich, forgiving faith.

In these jars is hidden treasure,
Costly fragrance, Christly pleasure,
Like the Christ, first from the dead,
Broken for creation's wholeness,
Poured out for its coming fullness,
Prophet, Servant, Hope, and Head.

Holy woman, costly treasure,
With the jar of alabaster,
Shows the hidden gift we are;
Therefore let us as Christ's servants
Hold our sister in remembrance,
Woman with the ointment jar.

HOLY WOMAN, GRACEFUL GIVER
(JOHN 12)

Holy woman, graceful giver,
Prophet, servant, and believer,
Mary with the ointment jar,
Sought the Christ, by scorn undaunted,
Knelt in love, his feet anointed
For his coming burial hour.

How the fragrance filled the dwelling!
How the act of beauty welling
Blest all those within the place!
How the act of pure devotion,
Whispering of his coming passion,
Blest the heart of Christ with grace!

Lovingly Christ stilled the scoffer
Who would grasping guard the coffer,
Pointing to a hidden trove:
Not all treasures gain and profit;
Feed the poor, and feed the spirit
Acts of beauty, acts of love.

Though disdained or though contested,
Acts of love are never wasted:
Beauty is a face of God.
Graceful Mary, by your giving,
You have shown a way of living:
Acts of beauty, love, and good.

HOW BEAUTIFUL, O GOD, HOW GOOD

How beautiful, O God, how good
This bountiful creation:
Abundant life, abundant light,
Upheld by your compassion;
All things in you do live and move,
Existing by your boundless love.

How pleasant and how good it is
When people dwell in union,
And steadfast love and gentleness
Embody your communion:
Your Spirit grants the grace to share
And hope, to stand against despair.

How blest, O God, how blest are they
Who yearn, like you, for mercy,
Whose hearts, within your heart, find joy
In loving all and serving:
Where you in Christ our lives supply,
Five loaves and fishes multiply.

How steadfast is your love, O God,
Your deep desire pursues us;
That all may live their noble worth,
Inspire us, change us, use us,
That we, transformed, may live as Christ,
And all may know abundant life.

HOW LOVELY IS YOUR DWELLING PLACE

How lovely is your dwelling place,
O God of Hosts, O Sun of Grace,
Where heart and flesh may sing aloud
Glad praises to the living God.

There fainting souls their longing ease
Within your courts of holy peace;
The nesting swallow thence may come,
And smallest sparrow find a home.

How happy those who so may dwell
And sing from Zion's holy hill;
How blest the hearts that know the road,
Whose strength ascends from you, O God.

May all who sing your praises move
From strength to strength compelled by love,
And be fine temples of your grace,
A fair and lovely dwelling place.

How lovely is your dwelling place,
O God of Hosts, O Sun of Grace,
Where heart and flesh may sing aloud
Glad praises to the living God.

HOW SHALL WE SEE THE REALM OF GOD?

How shall we see the realm of God?
A seed so small it scarce is seen,
Yet grows a tree so tall and broad,
A gracious refuge full and green:
There birds can nest among its boughs
And larks and sparrows find a house.
       O grant us wonder, God, that we
       May signs of your unfolding see.

The realm of God, it is as yeast
A woman mixed into the meal
That proofed and hidden, thus increased,
A risen, leavened loaf to yield:
And from this blest, abundant bread
The hungry ones may all be fed.
       O grant us meekness, God, that we
       May signs of your uprising see.

The realm of God is as a pearl,
Or treasure in the soil concealed,
So rare and of such priceless worth,
All else is sold to buy the field:
Great joy shall mark the sacrifice
That buys the pearl beyond all price.
       O grant us wisdom, God, that we
       May signs of your abundance see.

The realm of God is as a net
That drags the fathoms of the deep,
Ingathers fish and flotsam both,
The some to cast, the some to keep:
And God alone will sort the trove
With holy will and steadfast love.
       O grant us mercy, God, that we
       May signs of your compassion see.

Your realm shall come, O God, on earth:
As growing seed, as rising bread,
As treasure found, as priceless pearl,
As harvest of the trolling net:
An active Godly growing sphere,
Until your realm at last is here.
       O grant us open hearts, that we
       May vessels of your coming be.

HOW WONDROUS IS YOUR STEADFAST LOVE

How wondrous is your steadfast love,
O God, in whom we live and move;
Your loving voice spoke forth the Light
And sang the sun against the night;
All time, all years turned at your will
And move within your loving still.

Your love encircles earth around:
The breathing air, the greening ground,
The teeming wild, the beating heart,
Infused, enlivened by your art;
In you alone all things increase
And fashion from each place a feast.

In you, in you alone we live:
Each day a feast, each breath a gift,
And in your Christ, O God, we view
How Love is making all things new:
Each day transformed; transfused, each place;
Each life transfigured by your grace.

So set in us your Spirit's power
That steadfast love direct each hour;
So speak in us your holy will
That from your feast all shall be filled,
For, God, in you we live and move,
And wondrous is your steadfast love!

IN LOVE GOD IMAGINED THE WORLDS TO LIGHT

In love God imagined the worlds to light;
God's love all creation upholds;
God joys in the dancing of day and night,
Delights as life's wonders unfold.
    So let us sing Wonder
    And let us sing Love
    And let us sing God above all.

God stirs in the yearning toward truth and peace;
God breathes in the prayers of the saint;
No failing, no falter God's love decrease:
God holds the right hand of the faint.
    So let us sing Steadfast
    And let us sing Care
    And let us sing God above all.

In Christ God ennobles all human worth;
God's Spirit enflames heart and frame,
Transforming the journey, renewing earth,
Transfigured by God's holy Name.
    So let us sing Service
    And let us sing Life
    And let us sing God above all.

So deeper in truth let us seek and move,
And broader in service and care,
Still stronger in union through God's own love,
For where there is love, God is there.
    So let us sing Promise
    And let us sing Hope
    And let us sing God above all.

LIKE MORNING DEW AFRESH UPON THE MOUNT

Like morning dew afresh upon the mount,
And precious oil so fragrant on the face,
How good it is, how pleasant unto God,
When holy friendship dwells within a place:
And on this mount, a feast, rich feast, for all.

O treasure far beyond the heart's request:
The meal, the well-aged wine, the broken bread—
And we, once longing, now belonging guests,
Become transfigured by the food we're fed:
And on this mount a feast, rich feast, for all.

Now living, fed and formed by holy food,
Abrim with Spirit, leavened by the Christ,
How good it is, how pleasant unto God,
When open hands serve gladly without price:
And on this mount, a feast, rich feast, for all.

Grant us, O God of Hosts, your loving will,
New hearts and eyes to see you in each face,
That in procession up your holy hill,
All peoples may ascend and sing your praise:
And on this mount, your feast, O God, for all.

NO WORD EXPRESSES YOU, O GOD

No word expresses you, O God,
No song can fully praise,
No mind can fathom full your Word,
No eye behold your gaze:
Yet from your love we live and grow
And gratefully our praise bestow.

You spoke and daylight darkness broke,
You blest, and earth did yield,
You breathed, and humankind awoke
Sustained by fruit and field:
Each dawn a gift, each vista gold,
Each day your wonders we behold.

In Christ you came on earth to dwell,
Humanity embraced;
In speaking, blessing, making well
Embodied love and grace,
And Christ, by cross and empty tomb,
Past fear and death now bids us come.

We come, O God, by Spirit blest,
To Christly lives of grace,
To fearless lives of gentleness,
To harvest lives of peace:
Each life a gift, each story gold,
Each one belovèd in your fold.

No word expresses you, O God,
No song can fully praise,
No mind can fathom full your Word,
No eye behold your gaze:
Yet with the saints we bend the knee
And praise you, Holy Trinity!

O CHRIST, UNTO YOUR CROSS WE RAISE

O Christ, unto your cross we raise
Our eyes in gratitude and praise,
And lift up holy hands in prayer
For what your grace embodied there:
A heart of love, so high, so broad—
The unrelenting love of God.

To you, O Christ, we lift our days
To be the vessels of your grace;
Drawn to your cross, our lives redrawn,
We serve the world unto your dawn;
Fed at your meal, we turn to feed
All those in hunger, those in need.

Your outstretched arms embrace the world
To which in mercy we are called;
May we take up your cross, O Christ,
To take up lives of sacrifice,
And follow in your selfless path
That draws abundant life from death.

This cross can call, this cross can prove
A sign of God's unchanging love;
Lift up our hearts, transfigure us
Into the pattern of your cross;
So may our hearts receive this sign,
And so embody love divine.

O GOD, GREAT LOVE, MOST RADIANT, BRIGHT

O God, great Love, most radiant, bright,
Whose truth flared all things into light,
Be ever in our hearts as flame
And show the wonders of your Name.

O Christ, O loving flashing-forth,
In whom God's brightness shone on earth,
Be now for us the Morning Star
And light to every season bear.

O Holy Spirit, joyous Fire,
Indwelling of God's deep desire,
Be here our foundry; fire us through
And cast us all as Christ anew.

Now let all hearts the Maker praise,
One God, who tenders all our days:
One radiant Love, one Fire, one Sun,
Creator, Christ, and Spirit, One.

O GOD OF FIRE, O WORD OF FLAME

O God of Fire, O Word of Flame,
That calls each creature's precious name,
As once you came, come now, inspire,
That we become on earth your fire.

Pour out your Spirit on all flesh;
Ignite in us enlightened speech,
That, thus enkindled by your spark,
We speak the language of each heart.

Remove from us all dross and fear,
And with your burning love draw near,
That as your first-fruits we emerge
Refined, transfigured from your forge.

Enfold us in your warm embrace,
That we become your dwelling place,
And as your holy mortal home,
A welcome hearth to all become.

So change us, charge us, that we move
As sanctuaries of your love,
And in these latter days inspire,
That we become on earth your fire.

O GOD OF WONDERS

O God of Wonders, by whose loving Word
The rivers course, the hawks soar to the height,
Draw us to wonder, so to see your world
Inspired by beauty, wakened by your light.

> *Refrain*
> May mindful praise to God sing out Amen
> And make of all our days a thankful hymn.

Whatever true is, noble, pure and right,
Encompass us and shape our every quest;
The mind of Christ be in our searching mind;
The heart of Christ, an ever-present guest.   *Refrain*

Within these walls may our becoming prove
A journey deep and deeper into you,
That, wise and faithful, we may serve and love
Your whole creation, and so honor you.   *Refrain*

O HEART OF GOD

O Heart of God, O Chamber of the Holy,
O Deepest Love, O Fount of loving Grace,
Not far in deepest space nor reaches lonely
Shall we seek out your holy dwelling place—
Your Word, your world, your Christ have shown us this:
Your heartbeat sounds in everything that is.

The world you weave, O God, a marvelous wonder:
The smallest spark communing with the whole;
One holy web of interwoven ardor,
One holy God, its unencompassed Soul.
Your Word, your world, your Christ have shown us this:
Your heartbeat sounds in everything that is.

No person's eyes but see by your own visage;
No person's heart beats separate from your will;
Each person is created in your image:
Each life, each death entangled with us all.
Your Word, your world, your Christ have shown us this:
Your heartbeat sounds in everything that is.

In you our prayers resound in all creation;
The seen and unseen echo our intent;
Your heart is moved, O God, and Spirit beckons
Our hearts to change, our actions to transcend.
Your Word, your world, your Christ have shown us this:
Your heartbeat sounds in everything that is.

Your dwelling place, O God, is among mortals;
The earth is yours, and nowhere are you not;
The stranger's face, the aching earth, are portals,
And there we see you, Love we long have sought.
O Heart of God, O Deepest Love, be praised:
Your heartbeat sounds in everything that is.

O INFINITE GREATNESS, O LIMITLESS GOOD

O Infinite Greatness, O Limitless Good,
Imbuing creation with glory and gold,
Great God, with the angels proclaiming Your peace,
We hallow Your Name in this luminous feast:
Gloria!

O Beautiful Mother, O Dwelling of God,
In strength and in dignity you are enrobed;
And shelter the Heart of the World at your breast;
So magnify with us this luminous feast:
Gloria!

O Word Made Incarnate, O Sun of Delight,
Dispelling the dark with compassion and Light;
Divine common hope of the poor and the least,
We witness Your dawn on this luminous feast:
Gloria!

O Dwelling of Glory, O People of Morn,
The Holy One ever desires to be born;
So may we, like Mary, enfold God the Guest,
And greet with rejoicing this luminous feast:
Gloria!

O NOT TO US

O not to us, O not to us
Should glory be proclaimed,
But, O Great God, to you alone,
And your majestic name.

The mountain heights, the depths of earth,
Spring not from our design,
But from your vast, creative word
And boundless love divine.

Our every breath draws from your love,
All art, all sense, all skill;
Your steadfast love is source and hope,
Your presence, help and shield.

Awake, O harp and lyre, awake;
We will awake the dawn!
And, trusting in the living God,
Sing ever and sing on.

To you alone, to you alone,
All glory be proclaimed,
For you are God, the Holy One,
And glorious is your name.

SHALL I NOT PRAISE GOD WITH SINGING?

Shall I not praise God with singing?
Shall I not in God be glad?
For all things from God proceeding
Prove his purpose for my good.
It is nought but lovingkindness
That his faithful heart controls,
That unceasing lifts and holds
Those who practice in his service.
All things for a time endure,
God's love lasts forevermore.

As an eagle spreads its feathers
Shielding young from storm and harm,
So through life I have found shelter
Safe in God Almighty's arm,
Like a mother's deep devotion,
Since my life to me he gave
And this being that I have,
And still sets the hours in motion.
All things for a time endure,
God's love lasts forevermore.

God's own Son is not too treasured,
No, he gives him up for me,
That I may from fiery torture
By his blood delivered be.
O eternal flowing Fountain!
How then will my spirit weak,
Even though it search and seek,
Ever full your deepness fathom?
All things for a time endure,
God's love lasts forevermore.

And his Spirit, noble mentor,
In his word God does impart,
That I, governed well, may enter
From this world to heaven's court,
That my heart may be enlightened
With the brightest light of faith
That destroys the power of death,
So that hell itself falls silent.
All things for a time endure,
God's love lasts forevermore.

The well-being of my spirit
God has rightly born in mind,
To my flesh, should need impair it,
God will there his gaze incline.
If my craft, my power, my knowing
Nothing solve and nothing help,
God comes forth and lifts me up,
Glory, might, and power foregoing.
All things for a time endure,
God's love lasts forevermore.

Heaven, earth, and all their legions
God has planted to provide,
Everywhere I turn my vision
That which keeps and feeds I find:
Beast and blossom, grain and grasses,
In the ground and in the sky,
In the grove and in the sea:
Everywhere God gives me pasture.
All things for a time endure,
God's love lasts forevermore.

When I sleep, God's care attending
Cheers the heart and soul of me,
That each dawn as night is ending
Love and kindness new I see.
If my God had not existed,
Had his face not guided me,
I, mere mortal, could not be
Out of so much fear assisted.
All things for a time endure,
God's love lasts forevermore.

Ah, how many woes are offered,
Trials from Satan are conveyed,
That I never yet have suffered,
Not in all my living days!
Angels sent from God, defending,
Turn the evil from the foe,
Served for me to undergo,
Into outer darkness sending.
All things for a time endure,
God's love lasts forevermore.

As a father from his offspring
Never would his love withhold,
Whether sometimes faced with sinning
Or a straying from the road:
So my faithful God considers
My offenses for my good,
Counters misdeeds with the rod,
Leaves the sword within the scabbard.
All things for a time endure,
God's love lasts forevermore.

But his punishment, his lashes,
Though they both may bitter tend,
After all is weighed and rationed,
They are signs that this my friend,
This my friend, the one who loves me,
Wills, from self and thought in thrall
To the world so base and small,
Steady toward the cross to move me.
All things for a time endure,
God's love lasts forevermore.

This I know and hold in reason,
Will not let it leave my mind:
That the cross, it has its season,
And at last must step aside.
When the winter snows are melting,
Lovely summer enters in;
So it also is with pain:
Who endures, goes out exulting.
All things for a time endure,
God's love lasts forevermore.

Thus since neither end nor ceasing
God's love ever can imbue,
Ah, indeed! my hands are raising,
Father, as a child to you.
Pray, may grace to me be given,
With my power and my might
To embrace you day and night
Here in every day of living,
Till I past this time endure,
Praise and love you evermore.

PAUL GERHARDT, 1607-1676
TR. © 2014 SUSAN PALO CHERWIEN, ADMIN. AUGSBURG FORTRESS

SING, OH, SING THE THREEFOLD GOD

Sing, oh, sing the threefold God,
Unending Fount of goodness,
Root of this becoming world:
God is gracious.

Sing as one God's boundless grace
At play in all creation,
Holy Heart of time and space:
God who made us.

Sing aloud the love of Christ,
The face of God incarnate,
Cross of selfless sacrifice:
God among us.

Sing anew the Spirit's power
That calls, enfolds, enlightens,
Forging with transforming fire:
God within us.

Sing, O people, sing God's grace—
Creator, Christ, and Spirit,
Deigning here a dwelling place:
God is with us!

SPIRIT OF GOD, RESOUND IN US

Spirit of God, resound in us
With songs of beauty, hymns of life,
That beauty from our voices rise
In echoed tones melodious;
Alleluia.

Spirit of God, revive in us
Our first and given Godly state,
That with the One we may create
A world divine and marvelous;
Alleluia.

Spirit of God, reveal in us
The boundless Good that knows no shore,
And spur our actions to explore
God's all-embracing spaciousness;
Alleluia.

Spirit of God, refine in us
The love of God, the mind of Christ,
That from all dross we be enticed
To lives all lovely, luminous;
Alleluia.

Spirit of God, reflect in us
The concord of God's living choir
That with the water, earth, wind, fire
We sing in praise harmonious;
Alleluia.

WHAT JOYOUS SONG UNFOLDING

What joyous song unfolding
Has called us in the night;
What loving voice imploring
Has drawn us into light:
The voice of God is singing,
The heartbeat of the spheres;
It echoes in all being
And calls us still to hear.

The mountains sing the story;
The forests clap their hands;
The stars sing forth God's glory;
The seas, the hills, the lands.
Shall we alone be silent?
Shall we not sing God's praise,
Whose song is ever present,
Whose voice enchants our days?

Then let us breathe together
To praise the God of Life,
And so conspire to sunder
Disharmony and strife,
That sighing cede to singing,
And beauty life renew;
That wisdom tune our being,
And love all fear subdue.

God, may our hearts be grateful,
And may our words be true.
May all our songs be noble
And draw us deep in you,
That singing holy stories,
More holy we become,
Transposed into like spirits
To be your loving home.

WHO IS THIS, THAT WINDS OBEY HIM

Who is this, that winds obey him,
Seas grow silent, storms grow still?
Who, awaking, soothes to sleeping
Gale and tempest by his will?
Christ it is, whose ever-presence
Quiets fright and calms our fear;
Christ it is, who offers haven:
Peace, be still, for I am here.

Mighty waters may dishearten,
Towering waves may crash and move,
But no wildness, nor thick darkness,
Shall subdue God's steadfast love.
God it is, who set sea's limits:
"Thus far shall you come—thus far";
God it is, who speaks and quiets:
Peace, be still, for I am here.

Why then fear when storms are raging,
When the primal seas assail?
God has spoken from the whirlwind;
Christ has spoken from the gale.
Now, the still point of deliverance;
Now the calms of peace appear,
For God's steadfast love says ever:
Peace, be still, for I am here.

HYMNS WITH MUSIC

ABIDE IN US, O BREAD OF LIFE

1 A - bide in us, O Bread of Life, That we a - bide in
2 True food in - fuse our ver - y flesh; True drink our days re -
3 Now for the jour - ney streng - then us; Your Heart in us in -
4 So change us by this ho - ly grace, This gift of love out -

You, And we in tak - ing bread par - take Of all that
vive, As in Your - self we find our - selves And You in
crease, That here Your Spir - it may a - bide And make each
poured, That we be - come Your bread on earth And live for

[1-3]
is in You.
us give life.
day a feast.

[4]
all the world.

Text: Susan Palo Cherwien
Music: David Cherwien

FEAST OF LIFE
8 6 8 6

ALL-EMBRACING GOD

1 All - em-brac-ing God, Build-er of all worlds,
2 All - em-brac-ing Christ, Ser - vant of all worlds,
3 All - em-brac-ing Fire, Spir - it of all worlds,
4 All - em-brac-ing church, Gath - ered from all worlds,
5 All - em-brac-ing God, Trin - i - ty of Love,

In your house your peo - ple rise to praise;
Hum - bly seek - ing out the last and least,
Prod - ding all God's peo - ple to e - volve,
Tem - ple of the Fire, the Love, the Name,
Dwell with - in us now, do not de - lay;

By your Ho - ly Name Signed and marked and sealed,
By your Ho - ly Love Signed and marked and sealed,
By your Ho - ly Gifts Signed and marked and sealed,
By the font and meal Signed and marked and sealed,
Make your church a - live With your ver - y life

Text: Susan Palo Cherwien
Music: Frank W. Boles
Text © 2016 Susan Palo Cherwien, admin. Augsburg Fortress
Music © 2016 Frank W. Boles, admin. Augsburg Fortress. All rights reserved.

VIRGINIA SQUARE
559559

May our hearts be - come your dwell - ing place.
May we strive for jus - tice and for peace.
May we seek and serve all that you love.
May we in fair lives God's grace pro - claim.
In the Now that does not pass a -

way.

AS YOUR SPIRIT IN THE DESERT

Cantor or choir

1 As your Spir-it in the des-ert Led the Christ to dust and
2 As your fire and cloud-y pil-lar Is-rael's tribes to Ca-naan
3 Though wild beasts may lurk in shad-ow, And dire thirst may sear and
4 Through the nar-row gate now draw us, Past all em-pire's pull and
5 God of Des-ert, God of Prom-ise, You have bid us jour-ney

stone, So in-still our hearts with cour-age Now to
led, May your pres-ence be our com-fort, May your
sting, You have prom-ised liv-ing wa-ters Wait-ing
strife, Where be-yond our fear and cling-ing Stands the
on Through the days of dust and dark-ness To the

Assembly

cross where Christ has gone. Let us cross in-to the
man-na be our bread. Let us cross in-to the
for us at the spring. Let us cross out of the
thresh-old of new life. Let us cross out of the
ris-ing of the dawn. Let us cross out of the

Text: Susan Palo Cherwien
Music: Michael D. Costello
Text © 2012 Susan Palo Cherwien, admin. Augsburg Fortress
Music © 2015 Augsburg Fortress. All rights reserved.

ROSEVILLE
878797

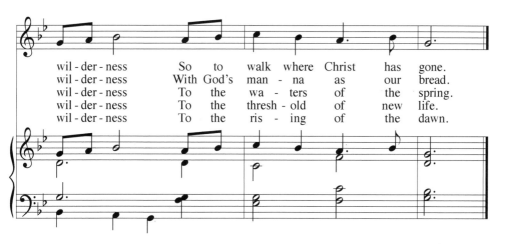

wil - der - ness | So | to | walk where Christ | has | gone.
wil - der - ness | With | God's | man - na | as | our | bread.
wil - der - ness | To | the | wa - ters | of | the | spring.
wil - der - ness | To | the | thresh - old | of | new | life.
wil - der - ness | To | the | ris - ing | of | the | dawn.

BEHOLD THE LILIES OF THE FIELD

1 Behold the lilies of the field, Be-
2 Behold the singing birds of air, A-
3 Why, then, by cares and dread consumed? Why
4 O hope in God, the living God, In
5 So let the morrow's sun arise; With

robed in raiment fair: They do not loom or
loft in joyful flight: Upheld by God's un-
so cast down, distressed? If God so cares for
whom all live and move; Each precious day be
joy its light caress, For God, all-loving,

spindle wield, Yet bloom without a care.
flagging care, They soar in God's delight.
bird and bloom, Will God regard you less?
met with awe; Each precious face, with love.
caring, wise, Will comfort and will bless.

Text: Susan Palo Cherwien
Music: Jonathan D. Campbell
Text © 2012 Susan Palo Cherwien, admin. Augsburg Fortress
Music © 2012 Jonathan D. Campbell, admin. Augsburg Fortress. All rights reserved.

TRUDY
C M

BEYOND THE MIND'S IMAGINING

1 Be - yond the mind's im - ag - in - ing, Be - yond the heart's de-
2 En - heart-ened by Christ's self - less life, May we Christ's love en-
3 Em - bold - ened by the Spir - it's gifts, A - fire with God's own
4 Where stone on stone our lives shall build, Though storm or sun shall

sire, The pow'r of God to love and bless, To
shrine, And gath - ered in Christ's ho - ly name Un -
grace, May we true love and wis - dom learn With -
pass, May ev - 'ry gen - er - a - tion praise, May

pros - per and in - spire, Be here a - mong us
fold to the Di - vine, By sa - cred sto - ry,
in God's warm em - brace, And thus true faith - ful
God's great name be blessed. That first and most with -

nur - tur - ing Our hearts with ho - ly fire.
ho - ly song, Sweet wa - ter and sweet wine.
ser - vants prove Through ev - 'ry time and place.
in each heart God's love may dwell at last.

Text: Susan Palo Cherwien
Music: David Cherwien
Text © 2013 Susan Palo Cherwien, admin. Augsburg Fortress
Music © 2013 David Cherwien, admin. Augsburg Fortress. All rights reserved.

SEWICKLEY
868686

BLESSED ONE, PARAGON

Refrain

Bless - ed One, Par - a-gon, Ho - ly gate and ho-ly throne, Bear - er of the Mid-night Son, O Ho - ly Moth - er.

Text: Susan Palo Cherwien
Music: Scottish folk tune
Text © 2013 Susan Palo Cherwien, admin. Augsburg Fortress

CA' THE YOWES
6 7 7 5 and refrain

1 God in - vites, You re - quite, Ves - sel of the
2 At your vow, Ga - briel bows, Clois - ter of the
3 In your womb, God finds room, Burn - ing bush of
4 By your word, For the world, Tem - ple of the
5 Hope finds rest At your breast, Ha - ven of the

Gm   Eb   F   Bb   Gm

prom - ised Light, Shin - ing in - to earth - ly night,
bur - geoning bough, Com - pass - ing the Christ a - bout,
bright - est bloom, Flam - ing out, yet not con - sumed,
liv - ing Word, Bear - ing al - so sor - row's sword,
heav'n - ly Guest, Shel - ter - ing the in - fant blest,

F   Gm   Eb   Bb   Gm

to Refrain

O   ra - diant   Moth - er.
O   lov - ing   Moth - er.
O   won - drous   Moth - er.
O   val - iant   Moth - er.
O   gen - tle   Moth - er.

F   Bb   Gm

COME, O SPIRIT, COME TO US

VENI SANCTE SPIRITUS

1 Come, O Spir - it, come to us, Send - ing forth the
lu - mi - nous Ra-diance of your ho - ly light.

2 Come, O Par - ent of the Poor, Come, O gen - 'rous
Treas - ure-store, Come, O heart - il - lum - ing Light.

3 O most gra - cious Com - fort - er, Sweet and wel - come
Vis - i - tor, Sweet and sooth - ing Heal - ing Light.

4 In our la - bor, be our rest, In our tem - per,
tem - per-ance, In our tears, con - sol - ing sigh.

Text: Medieval sequence, tr. Susan Palo Cherwien
Music: Traditional
Text © 2013 Susan Palo Cherwien, admin. Augsburg Fortress

VENI SANCTE SPIRITUS
7 7 7

5 O most bless - ed Light of God, In our hearts make your a - bode, Fill - ing us with faith and sight.

6 Lest your will in us a - bide, Noth - ing does in us re - side, Noth - ing that is whole and right.

7 Cleanse all that is soiled, im - pure, Quench all that is dry and sere, Cure all that is mor - ti - fied.

8 Gen - tle what is stone in us, Kin - dle what is ice in us, Bri - dle what is lost and wild.

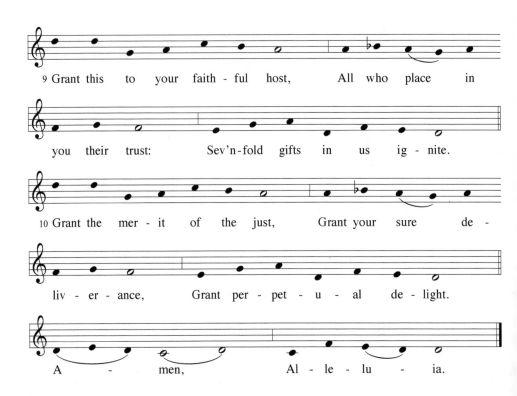

9 Grant this to your faith - ful host, All who place in
you their trust: Sev'n-fold gifts in us ig - nite.

10 Grant the mer - it of the just, Grant your sure de -
liv - er - ance, Grant per - pet - u - al de - light.

A - men, Al - le - lu - ia.

GOD HAS TOLD US, GOD HAS TAUGHT US

1 God has told us, God has taught us: "I am pres - ent;
2 Christ has shown us, Christ has taught us: "I am with you
3 God has shown us, Christ has taught us: "Know, Be - lov - ed,
4 There - fore, sis - ters, broth - ers, glad - ly May we love and

do not fear." God up - holds this lov - ing prom - ise:
age to age." As the vine is to the branch - es,
what is good": Do - ing jus - tice, lov - ing kind - ness,
trust in God, May we be as Christ's one bod - y,

"I am pres - ent, ev - er near." Look, be - hold, re -
Love sus - tains us all our days. Noth - ing parts us,
Walk - ing hum - bly with your God, Prod - ded by the
May we live the Spir - it's good, That our hearts be

ceive, be - lieve; Love and trust in God and live.
nor di - vides, From the love of God in Christ.
Spir - it's fire, Liv - ing out God's deep de - sire.
God's fair home, 'Til the reign of God shall come.

Text: Susan Palo Cherwien
Music: Scott M. Hyslop
Text © 2016 Susan Palo Cherwien, admin. Augsburg Fortress
Music © 2016 Scott M. Hyslop, admin. Selah Publishing Co.

PÍSTI, ELPÍDA, KAI AGÁPI
878777

GOD, WHO SET THE SPHERES IN MOTION

1 God, who set the spheres in mo - tion,
2 Thus when days and lives are pal - ing,
3 God, You bless us with com - pan - ions,
4 Thus through all the times and sea - sons

Times and sea - sons, dusk and dawn,
Death draws near us to em - brace,
Sis - ters, broth - ers, in this place;
To Your Name we lift our praise;

Ebb and tide of stream and o - cean,
May our peace - ful hearts un - fail - ing
We have sung them to Your man - sions
E - ven at the grave we sing it:

Turn and dance of star and sun,
Trust in Your un - chang - ing grace.
Where they dwell in Your em - brace.
Al - le - lu - ia, all our days.

Text: Susan Palo Cherwien
Music: William Bradley Roberts
Text © 2015 Susan Palo Cherwien, admin. Augsburg Fortress
Music © 2015 William Bradley Roberts, admin. Augsburg Fortress. All rights reserved.

LAFAYETTE SQUARE
8 7 8 7 D

All the turn - ing of cre - a - tion
As the win - ter turns at sol - stice,
Life in Christ leaves ho - ly path - ways;
Al - le - lu - ia, for the new - ness

Puls - es from Your heart sub - lime;
As the night turns t'ward the day,
Saint - ly signs lead us to see
Hid - den un - der twi - light's gray;

Ev - 'ry - thing, it has its sea - son,
All Your bless - ed sea - sons show us:
As their bless - ed lives bear wit - ness:
Al - le - lu - ia, for the prom - ise:

Ev - 'ry pur - pose has its time.
Life is changed, not swept a - way.
All streams run in - to the sea.
Life is changed, not swept a - way.

GREAT GOD, WHOSE STORY

1 Great God, whose sto-ry age to age Is sung by proph-et,
2 In depths of earth you wove each frame And called each pre-cious
3 The hymns of saints of yes-ter-days Still sound when we our
4 By song, by sign, by word, by meal Your lov-ing pres-ence

po-et, sage, Cre-a-tion's web, spun with your hands And
one by name; Now in your ho-ly courts we view How
voic-es raise; And gen-er-a-tions yet to be Take
is re-vealed; Oh, may our sto-ries join as one, Cre-

cast-ing in-to myr-iad strands, Tells out your love in
all your works are joined in you— A three-fold cord, not
hope in ev-'ry lit-a-ny; For through the Word, God
a-tor, Christ, and Spir-it, One, That we may weave through

time and space, A sto-ried tap-es-try of grace.
light un-done: Self, Neigh-bor, God, en-twined in one.
new cre-ates, The past and fu-ture, in-ter-laced.
end-less days A sto-ried tap-es-try of grace.

Text: Susan Palo Cherwien
Music: David Cherwien
Text © 2013 Susan Palo Cherwien, admin. Augsburg Fortress.
Music © 2013 David Cherwien, admin. Augsburg Fortress. All rights reserved.

EDMONTON NEW
888888

HOLY WOMAN, GRACEFUL GIVER (MARK 14)

1 Ho - ly wom - an, grace-ful giv - er, Proph - et, ser - vant, and be - liev - er, Wom-an with the oint - ment jar, Rose up near the time ap - point - ed, Broke the seal, Christ's

2 Like the ves - sel, we are bro - ken; Like the oint - ment, we are to - ken Of God's lov - ing un - to death; Like the wom - an, we are serv - ing; Like the scold - ers,

3 In these jars is hid - den treas - ure, Cost - ly fra - grance, Christ - ly pleas - ure, Like the Christ, first from the dead, Bro - ken for cre - a - tion's whole-ness, Poured out for its

4 Ho - ly wom - an, cost - ly treas - ure, With the jar of al - a - bas - ter, Shows the hid - den gift we are; There - fore let us as Christ's ser - vants Hold our sis - ter

Text: Susan Palo Cherwien
Music: David Cherwien
Text © 1994 Susan Palo Cherwien, admin. Augsburg Fortress
Music © 1995 Augsburg Fortress. All rights reserved.

ALABASTER
887887

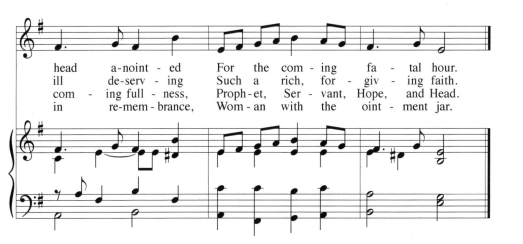

head   a-noint - ed   For   the com - ing   fa - tal hour.
ill   de-serv - ing   Such a   rich, for - giv - ing faith.
com - ing full - ness,   Proph - et, Ser - vant, Hope,   and Head.
in   re-mem - brance,   Wom - an with   the   oint - ment jar.

HOLY WOMAN, GRACEFUL GIVER (JOHN 12)

1 Ho - ly wom - an, grace - ful giv - er, Proph - et, ser - vant, and be - liev - er, Mar - y with the oint - ment jar, Sought the Christ, by scorn un - daunt - ed, Knelt in love, his

2 How the fra - grance filled the dwell - ing! How the act of beau - ty well - ing Blest all those with - in the place! How the act of pure de - vo - tion, Whis - p'ring of his

3 Lov - ing - ly Christ stilled the scoff - er Who would grasp - ing guard the cof - fer, Point - ing to a hid - den trove: Not all treas - ures gain and prof - it; Feed the poor, and

4 Though dis - dained or though con - test - ed, Acts of love are nev - er wast - ed: Beau - ty is a face of God. Grace - ful Mar - y, by your giv - ing, You have shown a

Text: Susan Palo Cherwien
Music: David Cherwien
Text © 2016 Susan Palo Cherwien, admin. Augsburg Fortress
Music © 1995 Augsburg Fortress. All rights reserved.

ALABASTER
887887

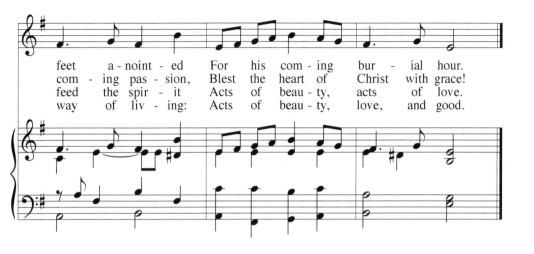

feet   a - noint - ed   For   his   com - ing   bur - ial   hour.
com - ing pas - sion,   Blest   the   heart   of   Christ   with grace!
feed   the   spir - it   Acts   of   beau - ty,   acts   of   love.
way   of   liv - ing: Acts   of   beau - ty,   love,   and good.

HOW BEAUTIFUL, O GOD, HOW GOOD

1 How beau - ti - ful, O God, how good This
2 How pleas - ant and how good it is When
3 How blest, O God, how blest are they Who
4 How stead - fast is your love, O God, Your

boun - ti - ful cre - a - tion: A - bun - dant life, a -
peo - ple dwell in u - nion, And stead - fast love and
yearn, like you, for mer - cy, Whose hearts, with - in your
deep de - sire pur - sues us; That all may live their

bun - dant light, Up - held by your com -
gen - tle - ness Em - bod - y your com -
heart, find joy In lov - ing all and
no - ble worth, In - spire us, change us,

Text: Susan Palo Cherwien
Music: David Cherwien
Text © 2015 Susan Palo Cherwien, admin. Augsburg Fortress
Music © 2015 David Cherwien, admin. Augsburg Fortress. All rights reserved.

NORELIUS
878788

78

pas - sion; All things in you do
mu - nion: Your Spir - it grants the
serv - ing: Where you in Christ our
use us, That we, trans-formed, may

live and move, Ex - ist - ing by your bound - less love.
grace to share And hope, to stand a - gainst de - spair.
lives sup - ply, Five loaves and fish - es mul - ti - ply.
live as Christ, And all may know a - bun - dant life.

HOW LOVELY IS YOUR DWELLING PLACE

1 How love - ly is your dwell - ing place, O
2 There faint - ing souls their long - ing ease With -
3 How hap - py those who so may dwell And
4 May all who sing your prais - es move From
5 How love - ly is your dwell - ing place, O

God of Hosts, O Sun of Grace, Where
in your courts of ho - ly peace; The
sing from Zi - on's ho - ly hill; How
strength to strength com - pelled by love, And
God of Hosts, O Sun of Grace, Where

heart and flesh may sing a - loud Glad
nest - ing swal - low thence may come, And
blest the hearts that know the road, Whose
be fine tem - ples of your grace, A
heart and flesh may sing a - loud Glad

Text: Susan Palo Cherwien
Music: Robert A. Hobby

TRINITY ENGLISH
LM

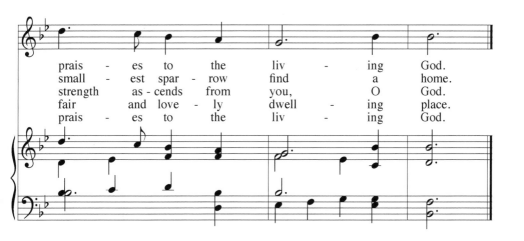

prais - es to the liv - ing God.
small - est spar - row find a home.
strength as - cends from you, O God.
fair and love - ly dwell - ing place.
prais - es to the liv - ing God.

HOW SHALL WE SEE THE REALM OF GOD?

1 How shall we see the realm of God? A
2 The realm of God, it is as yeast A
3 The realm of God is as a pearl, Or
4 The realm of God is as a net That
5 Your realm shall come, O God, on earth: As

seed so small it scarce is seen, Yet
wom - an mixed in - to the meal That
treas - ure in the soil con - cealed, So
drags the fath - oms of the deep, In -
grow - ing seed, as ris - ing bread, As

grows a tree so tall and broad, A
proofed and hid - den, thus in - creased, A
rare and of such price - less worth, All
gath - ers fish and flot - sam both, The
treas - ure found, as price - less pearl, As

gra - cious ref - uge full and green: There
ris - en, leav - ened loaf to yield: And
else is sold to buy the field: Great
some to cast, the some to keep: And
har - vest of the troll - ing net: An

Text: Susan Palo Cherwien
Music: Robert Buckley Farlee

IN PARABLES
888888

82

birds can nest a - mong its boughs And
from this blest, a - bun - dant bread The
joy shall mark the sac - ri - fice That
God a - lone will sort the trove With
ac - tive God - ly grow - ing sphere, Un -

larks and spar - rows find a house.
hun - gry ones may all be fed.
buys the pearl be - yond all price.
ho - ly will and stead - fast love.
til your realm at last is here.

O grant us won - der, God, that we May
O grant us meek - ness, God, that we May
O grant us wis - dom, God, that we May
O grant us mer - cy, God, that we May
O grant us o - pen hearts, that we May

signs of your un - fold - ing see.
signs of your up - ris - ing see.
signs of your a - bun - dance see.
signs of your com - pas - sion see.
ves - sels of your com - ing be.

83

HOW WONDROUS IS YOUR STEADFAST LOVE

1 How won-drous is your stead-fast love, O God, in
2 Your love en - cir - cles earth a - round: The breath-ing
3 In you, in you a - lone we live: Each day a
4 So set in us your Spir - it's pow'r That stead - fast

whom we live and move; Your lov - ing voice spoke forth the
air, the green - ing ground, The teem-ing wild, the beat-ing
feast, each breath a gift, And in your Christ, O God, we
love di - rect each hour; So speak in us your ho - ly

Light And sang the sun a - gainst the night; All time, all
heart, In - fused, en - liv - ened by your art; In you a -
view How Love is mak - ing all things new: Each day trans -
will That from your feast all shall be filled, For, God, in

Text: Susan Palo Cherwien
Music: David Cherwien
Text © 2014 Susan Palo Cherwien, admin. Augsburg Fortress
Music © 2014 David Cherwien, admin. Augsburg Fortress. All rights reserved.

SEANUEL
888888

years turned at your will And move with - in your
lone all things in - crease And fash - ion from each
formed; trans - fused, each place; Each life trans - fig - ured
you we live and move, And won - drous is your

lov - ing still.
place a feast.
by your grace.
stead - fast love!

IN LOVE GOD IMAGINED THE WORLDS TO LIGHT

1 In love God im-ag-ined the worlds to light;
2 God stirs in the yearn-ing toward truth and peace;
3 In Christ God en-no-bles all hu-man worth;
4 So deep-er in truth let us seek and move,

God's love all cre-a-tion up-holds;
God breathes in the prayers of the saint;
God's Spir-it en-flames heart and frame,
And broad-er in ser-vice and care,

God joys in the danc-ing of day and night,
No fail-ing, no fal-ter God's love de-crease:
Trans-form-ing the jour-ney, re-new-ing earth,
Still strong-er in u-nion through God's own love,

Text: Susan Palo Cherwien
Music: David Cherwien

HAYNIE
10 8 10 8 6 5 8

De - lights as life's won - ders un - fold.
God holds the right hand of the faint.
Trans - fig - ured by God's ho - ly Name.
For where there is love, God is there.

So let us sing Won - der And let us sing Love
So let us sing Stead - fast And let us sing Care
So let us sing Ser - vice And let us sing Life
So let us sing Prom - ise And let us sing Hope

And let us sing God a - bove all.

LIKE MORNING DEW AFRESH UPON THE MOUNT

1 Like morn-ing dew a-fresh up-on the mount, And
2 O treas-ure far be-yond the heart's re-quest: The
3 Now liv-ing, fed and formed by ho-ly food, A-
4 Grant us, O God of Hosts, your lov-ing will, New

pre-cious oil so fra-grant on the face, How good it
meal, the well-aged wine, the bro-ken bread— And we, once
brim with Spir-it, leav-ened by the Christ, How good it
hearts and eyes to see you in each face, That in pro-

is, how pleas-ant un-to God, When ho-ly friend-ship
long-ing, now be-long-ing guests, Be-come trans-fig-ured
is, how pleas-ant un-to God, When o-pen hands serve
ces-sion up your ho-ly hill, All peo-ples may as-

Text: Susan Palo Cherwien
Music: David Cherwien
Text © 2011 Susan Palo Cherwien, admin. Augsburg Fortress
Music © 2011 David Cherwien, admin. Augsburg Fortress. All rights reserved.

MM LONG
10 10 10 10 10 10

dwells with - in a place: And on this
by the food we're fed: And on this
glad - ly with - out price: And on this
cend and sing your praise: And on this

mount, a feast, rich feast, for all.
mount a feast, rich feast, for all.
mount, a feast, rich feast, for all.
mount, your feast, O God, for all.

NO WORD EXPRESSES YOU, O GOD

Text: Susan Palo Cherwien
Music: Scott M. Hyslop
Text © 2014 Susan Palo Cherwien, admin. Augsburg Fortress
Music © 2014 Scott M. Hyslop admin. Selah Publishing Co. All rights reserved.

BETHLEHEM, CHEROKEE
868688

eye be - hold your gaze: Yet from your
tained by fruit and field: Each dawn a
bod - ied love and grace, And Christ, by
har - vest lives of peace: Each life a
eye be - hold your gaze: Yet with the

love we live and grow And
gift, each vis - ta gold, Each
cross and emp - ty tomb, Past
gift, each sto - ry gold, Each
saints we bend the knee And

grate - ful - ly our praise be - stow.
day your won - ders we be - hold.
fear and death now bids us come.
one be - lov - ed in your fold.
praise you, Ho - ly Trin - i - ty!

91

O CHRIST, UNTO YOUR CROSS WE RAISE

1 O Christ, un - to your cross we raise Our
2 To you, O Christ, we lift our days To
3 Your out - stretched arms em - brace the world To
4 This cross can call, this cross can prove A

eyes in grat - i - tude and praise, And
be the ves - sels of your grace; Drawn
which in mer - cy we are called; May
sign of God's un - chang -ing love; Lift

lift up ho - ly hands in prayer For what your grace em -
to your cross, our lives re - drawn, We serve the world un -
we take up your cross, O Christ, To take up lives of
up our hearts, trans - fig - ure us In - to the pat - tern

Text: Susan Palo Cherwien
Music: David Cherwien

PORT CHARLOTTE
888888

bod - ied there: A   heart   of   love,   so
to   your   dawn;   Fed   at   your   meal,   we
sac - ri - fice,   And   fol - low   in   your
of   your   cross;   So   may   our   hearts   re -

high, so   broad—The   un - re - lent - ing   love   of   God.
turn   to   feed   All   those   in   hun - ger,   those   in   need.
self - less   path   That   draws   a - bun - dant   life   from   death.
ceive this   sign,   And   so   em - bod - y   love   di - vine.

O GOD, GREAT LOVE, MOST RADIANT, BRIGHT

1 O God, great Love, most ra - diant,
2 O Christ, O lov - ing flash - ing -
3 O Ho - ly Spir - it, joy - ous
4 Now let all hearts the Mak - er

bright, Whose truth flared all things in - to
forth, In whom God's bright - ness shone on
Fire, In - dwell - ing of God's deep de -
praise, One God, who ten - ders all our

light, Be ev - er in our hearts as
earth, Be now for us the Morn - ing
sire, Be here our found - ry; fire us
days: One ra - diant Love, one Fire, one

Text: Susan Palo Cherwien
Music: Scott M. Hyslop
Text © 2015 Susan Palo Cherwien, admin. Augsburg Fortress
Music © 2016 Scott M. Hyslop admin. Selah Publishing Co. All rights reserved.

GLADSTONE
LM

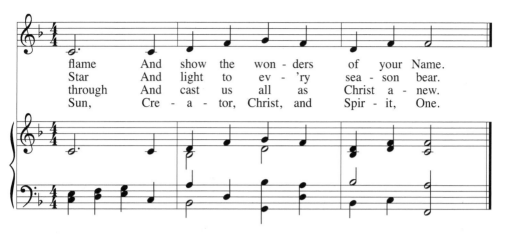

flame   And   show   the   won - ders   of   your   Name.
Star   And   light   to   ev - 'ry   sea - son   bear.
through   And   cast   us   all   as   Christ a - new.
Sun,   Cre - a - tor,   Christ,   and   Spir - it,   One.

O GOD OF FIRE, O WORD OF FLAME

1 O God of Fire, O Word of Flame, That calls each crea-ture's
2 Pour out your Spir - it on all flesh; Ig - nite in us en -
3 Re - move from us all dross and fear, And with your burn - ing
4 En - fold us in your warm em - brace, That we be - come your
5 So change us, charge us, that we move As sanc - tu - ar - ies

pre - cious name, As once you came, come now, in - spire,
light - ened speech, That, thus en - kin - dled by your spark,
love draw near, That as your first - fruits we e - merge
dwell - ing place, And as your ho - ly mor - tal home,
of your love, And in these lat - ter days in - spire,

That we be - come on earth your fire.
We speak the lan - guage of each heart.
Re - fined, trans - fig - ured from your forge.
A wel - come hearth to all be - come.
That we be - come on earth your fire. A - men.

Text: Susan Palo Cherwien
Music: Plainsong mode IV, arr. *Lutheran Book of Worship*
Text © 2011 Susan Palo Cherwien, admin. Augsburg Fortress
Arr. © 1978 *Lutheran Book of Worship*, admin. Augsburg Fortress. All rights reserved.

CONDITOR ALME SIDERUM
LM

O GOD OF WONDERS

1 O God of Wonders, by whose lov-ing Word The riv-ers course, the hawks soar to the height, Draw us to won-der, so to see your world In-spired by beau-ty, wak-ened by your light.

2 What-ev-er true is, no-ble, pure and right, The En-com-pass us and shape our ev-'ry quest; The mind of Christ be in our search-ing mind; The heart of Christ, an ev-er-pres-ent guest.

3 With-in these walls may our be-com-ing prove A jour-ney deep and deep-er in-to you, That, wise and faith-ful, we may serve and love Your whole cre-a-tion, and so hon-or you.

MINNEHAHA NEW
10 10 10 10 10 10

Refrain

May mind - ful praise to God sing out A - men And make of all our days a thank - ful hymn.

O HEART OF GOD

1 O Heart of God, O Cham-ber of the Ho-ly,
2 The world you weave, O God, a mar-v'lous won-der:
3 No per-son's eyes but see by your own vis-age;
4 In you our prayers re-sound in all cre-a-tion;
5 Your dwell-ing place, O God, is a-mong mor-tals;

O Deep-est Love, O Fount of lov-ing Grace,
The small-est spark com-mun-ing with the whole;
No per-son's heart beats sep-'rate from your will;
The seen and un-seen ech-o our in-tent;
The earth is yours, and no-where are you not;

Not far in deep-est space nor reach-es
One ho-ly web of in-ter-wo-ven
Each per-son is cre-at-ed in your
Your heart is moved, O God, and Spir-it
The stran-ger's face, the ach-ing earth, are

Text: Susan Palo Cherwien
Music: David Cherwien

PLYMOUTH
11 10 11 10 10 10

lone - ly Shall we seek out your ho - ly dwell - ing
ar - dor, One ho - ly God, its un - en - com - passed
im - age: Each life, each death en - tan - gled with us
beck - ons Our hearts to change, our ac - tions to tran -
por - tals, And there we see you, Love we long have

place— Your Word, your world, your Christ have shown us
Soul. Your Word, your world, your Christ have shown us
all. Your Word, your world, your Christ have shown us
scend. Your Word, your world, your Christ have shown us
sought. O Heart of God, O Deep - est Love, be

this:
this:
this: Your heart - beat sounds in ev - 'ry-thing that is.
this:
praised:

O INFINITE GREATNESS, O LIMITLESS GOOD

1 O In - fi - nite Great - ness, O Lim - it - less Good, Im - bu - ing cre - a - tion with glo - ry and gold, Great God, with the an - gels pro -

2 O Beau - ti - ful Moth - er, O Dwell - ing of God, In strength and in dig - ni - ty you are en - robed; And shel - ter the Heart of the

3 O Word Made In - car - nate, O Sun of De - light, Dis - pel - ling the dark with com - pas - sion and Light; Di - vine com - mon hope of the

4 O Dwell - ing of Glo - ry, O Peo - ple of Morn, The Ho - ly One ev - er de - sires to be born; So may we, like Mar - y, en -

Text: Susan Palo Cherwien
Music: David Cherwien

MARLIS
11 11 11 11 and Gloria

claim - ing Your peace, We hal - low Your Name in this
World at your breast; So mag - ni - fy with us this
poor and the least, We wit - ness Your dawn on this
fold God the Guest, And greet with re - joic - ing this

lu - mi - nous feast: Glo - ri - a! Glo - ri - a!

Glo - ri - a, glo - ri - a, glo - ri - a!

O NOT TO US

1 O not to us, O not to us Should
2 The moun-tain heights, the depths of earth, Spring
3 Our ev - 'ry breath draws from your love, All
4 A - wake, O harp and lyre, a - wake; We
5 To you a - lone, to you a - lone, All

glo - ry be pro - claimed, But, O Great God, to
not from our de - sign, But from your vast, cre -
art, all sense, all skill; Your stead - fast love is
will a - wake the dawn! And, trust - ing in the
glo - ry be pro - claimed, For you are God, the

you a - lone, And your ma - jes - tic name.
a - tive word And bound - less love di - vine.
source and hope, Your pres - ence, help and shield.
liv - ing God, Sing ev - er and sing on.
Ho - ly One, And glo - rious is your name.

Text: Susan Palo Cherwien
Music: Scott M. Hyslop
Text © 2012 Susan Palo Cherwien, admin. Augsburg Fortress
Music © 2012 Scott M. Hyslop, admin. Selah Publishing Co. All rights reserved.

NOT TO US
CM

SHALL I NOT PRAISE GOD WITH SINGING

1 Shall I not praise God with sing-ing? Shall I
2 As an ea-gle spreads its feath-ers Shield-ing
3 God's own Son is not too treas-ured, No, he
4 And his Spir-it, no-ble men-tor, In his

not in God be glad? For all things from God pro-
young from storm and harm, So through life I have found
gives him up for me, That I may from fi-'ry
word God does im-part, That I, gov-erned well, may

ceed-ing Prove his pur-pose for my good.
shel-ter Safe in God Al-might-y's arm.
tor-ture By his blood de-liv-ered be.
en-ter From this world to heav-en's court,

It is nought but lov-ing-kind-ness That his
Like a moth-er's deep de-vo-tion, Since my
O e-ter-nal flow-ing Foun-tain! How then
That my heart may be en-light-ened With the

Text: Paul Gerhardt, 1607–1676; tr. Susan Palo Cherwien
Music: Johann Schop, c. 1590–1667
Text © 2014 Susan Palo Cherwien, admin. Augsburg Fortress

SOLLT ICH MEINEM GOTT
8 7 8 7 8 7 7 7 7 7

faith - ful heart con - trols, That un - ceas - ing
life to me he gave And this be - ing
will my spir - it weak, E - ven though it
bright - est light of faith That de - stroys the

lifts and holds Those who prac - tice in his ser - vice.
that I have, And still sets the hours in mo - tion.
search and seek, Ev - er full your deep - ness fath - om?
pow'r of death, So that hell it - self falls si - lent.

All things for a time en - dure,

God's love lasts for - ev - er - more.

5 The well-being of my spirit
   God has rightly born in mind,
   To my flesh, should need impair it,
   God will there his gaze incline.
   If my craft, my pow'r, my knowing
   Nothing solve and nothing help,
   God comes forth and lifts me up,
   Glory, might, and pow'r foregoing.
   All things for a time endure,
   God's love lasts forevermore.

6 Heaven, earth, and all their legions
   God has planted to provide,
   Ev'rywhere I turn my vision
   That which keeps and feeds I find:
   Beast and blossom, grain and grasses,
   In the ground and in the sky,
   In the grove and in the sea:
   Ev'rywhere God gives me pasture.
   All things for a time endure,
   God's love lasts forevermore.

7 When I sleep, God's care attending
   Cheers the heart and soul of me,
   That each dawn as night is ending
   Love and kindness new I see.
   If my God had not existed,
   Had his face not guided me,
   I, mere mortal, could not be
   Out of so much fear assisted.
   All things for a time endure,
   God's love lasts forevermore.

8 Ah, how many woes are offered,
   Trials from Satan are conveyed,
   That I never yet have suffered,
   Not in all my living days!
   Angels sent from God, defending,
   Turn the evil from the foe,
   Served for me to undergo,
   Into outer darkness sending.
   All things for a time endure,
   God's love lasts forevermore.

9 As a father from his offspring
   Never would his love withhold,
   Whether sometimes faced with sinning
   Or a straying from the road:
   So my faithful God considers
   My offenses for my good,
   Counters misdeeds with the rod,
   Leaves the sword within the scabbard.
   All things for a time endure,
   God's love lasts forevermore.

10 But his punishment, his lashes,
   Though they both may bitter tend,
   After all is weighed and rationed,
   They are signs that this my friend,
   This my friend, the one who loves me,
   Wills, from self and thought in thrall
   To the world so base and small,
   Steady toward the cross to move me.
   All things for a time endure,
   God's love lasts forevermore.

11 This I know and hold in reason,
   Will not let it leave my mind:
   That the cross, it has its season,
   And at last must step aside.
   When the winter snows are melting,
   Lovely summer enters in;
   So it also is with pain:
   Who endures, goes out exulting.
   All things for a time endure,
   God's love lasts forevermore.

12 Thus since neither end nor ceasing
   God's love ever can imbue,
   Ah, indeed! my hands are raising,
   Father, as a child to you.
   Pray, may grace to me be given,
   With my power and my might
   To embrace you day and night
   Here in ev'ry day of living,
   Till I past this time endure,
   Praise and love you evermore.

SING, OH, SING, THE THREEFOLD GOD

Text: Susan Palo Cherwien
Music: David Cherwien
Text © 2015 Susan Palo Cherwien, admin. Augsburg Fortress
Music © 2015 David Cherwien, admin. Augsburg Fortress. All rights reserved.

GRACE UNENDING
7 7 7 4

God   is   gra - cious.
God   who   made   us.
God   a - mong   us.
God   with - in   us.
God   is   with   us!

SPIRIT OF GOD, RESOUND IN US

1 Spir-it of God, re - sound in us With
2 Spir-it of God, re - vive in us Our
3 Spir-it of God, re - veal in us The
4 Spir-it of God, re - fine in us The
5 Spir-it of God, re - flect in us The

songs of beau - ty, hymns of life, That
first and giv - en God - ly state, That
bound-less Good that knows no shore, And
love of God, the mind of Christ, That
con - cord of God's liv - ing choir That

ANNO TRINGINTA QUINQUE
LM and alleluias

beau - ty from our voic - es rise In ech - oed tones me -
with the One we may cre - ate A world di - vine and
spur our ac - tions to ex - plore God's all - em - brac - ing
from all dross we be en - ticed To lives all love - ly,
with the wa - ter, earth, wind, fire We sing in praise har -

lo - di - ous;
mar - vel - ous;
spa - cious - ness;   Al - le - lu - ia.
lu - mi - nous;
mo - ni - ous;

Al - le - lu - ia.   Al - le - lu - ia.

WHAT JOYOUS SONG UNFOLDING

1 What joy - ous song un - fold - ing Has called us in the night;
2 The moun - tains sing the sto - ry; The for - ests clap their hands;
3 Then let us breathe to - geth - er To praise the God of Life,
4 God, may our hearts be grate - ful, And may our words be true.

What lov - ing voice im - plor - ing Has drawn us in - to light:
The stars sing forth God's glo - ry; The seas, the hills, the lands.
And so con - spire to sun - der Dis - har - mo - ny and strife,
May all our songs be no - ble And draw us deep in you,

The voice of God is sing - ing, The heart - beat of the spheres;
Shall we a - lone be si - lent? Shall we not sing God's praise,
That sigh - ing cede to sing - ing, And beau - ty life re - new;
That sing - ing ho - ly sto - ries, More ho - ly we be - come,

It ech - oes in all be - ing And calls us still to hear.
Whose song is ev - er pre - sent, Whose voice en - chants our days?
That wis - dom tune our be - ing, And love all fear sub - due.
Trans - posed in - to like spir - its To be your lov - ing home.

Text: Susan Palo Cherwien
Music: Finnish folk tune, arr. *Lutheran Book of Worship*
Text © 2011 Susan Palo Cherwien, admin. Augsburg Fortress
Arr. © 1978 *Lutheran Book of Worship*, admin. Augsburg Fortress.

NOORMARKKU
7 6 7 6 D

WHO IS THIS, THAT WINDS OBEY HIM

1 Who is this, that winds o - bey him,
2 Might - y wa - ters may dis - heart - en,
3 Why then fear when storms are rag - ing,

Seas grow si - lent, storms grow still?
Tow'r - ing waves may crash and move,
When the pri - mal seas as - sail?

Who, a - wak - ing, soothes to sleep - ing
But no wild - ness, nor thick dark - ness,
God has spo - ken from the whirl - wind;

Text: Susan Palo Cherwien
Music: Timothy J. Strand
Text © 2015 Susan Palo Cherwien, admin. Augsburg Fortress
Music © 2015 Timothy J. Strand, admin. Augsburg Fortress. All rights reserved.

PREISINGER
8 7 8 7 D

Gale and tem - pest by his will?
Shall sub - due God's stead - fast love.
Christ has spo - ken from the gale.

Christ it is, whose ev - er - pres - ence
God it is, who set sea's lim - its:
Now, the still point of de - liv - 'rance;

Qui - ets fright and calms our fear;
"Thus far shall you come— thus far";
Now the calms of peace ap - pear,

Christ it is, who of - fers ha - ven:
God it is, who speaks and qui - ets:
For God's stead - fast love says ev - er:

Peace, be still, for I am here.

APPENDIXES

BACKGROUND OF THE TEXTS

Abide in Us, O Bread of Life

The August 2015 wedding of our son, Benjamin, and daughter-in-law, Angel, fell at the end of the many John 6 Sundays in year B of the Revised Common Lectionary. Since Angel and Benjamin are both chefs, it seemed fitting to use the Bread of Life and feast imagery of John 6 for this gift for their wedding liturgy.

August 13, 2015
8.6.8.6 iambic
Based on John 6 and a sermon by Pastor Joseph Crippen on August 9, 2015

All-embracing God

Commissioned by St. George's Episcopal Church, Arlington, Virginia, for the rededication of the church sanctuary in 2016.
Based on 2 Corinthians 5, Ezra 3, the Baptismal Covenant in the Book of Common Prayer, and the fifth-century prayer of Balai, chorepiscopos of Aleppo: "May the temples built within ourselves be as beautiful as the temple built of stone. May your kindness impel you to live in both kinds of temple, for our hearts, no less than these stones, bear the mark of your Name."

After completing the hymn, I learned that Balai was known for his metrical use of five, and he also wrote a hymn to St. George. The word *katholikos* means "all-embracing." "The Now that does not pass away" is from Augustine's *nunc stans*, quoted by Brother David Steindl-Rast.

March 3, 2016
5.5.9.5.5.9 trochaic

As Your Spirit in the Desert

This litany uses the images from the Lent year B pericopes to portray Lent as a journey from desert to new life, from bondage to freedom, from thirst to living water, and from darkness to new dawn. Commissioned by St.

Michael's Lutheran Church, Roseville, Minnesota, in memory of Thomas Klug.

8.7.8.7 with refrain 9.7 (anapest with trochees)
Based on the Lenten pericopes for the Year of Mark

Behold the Lilies of the Field
In October 2011, Rochester, Minnesota, church musician Jon Strommen Campbell requested a text on healing for his mother's ongoing experience with cancer, but at Trudy H. Enstad Campbell's early death in January 2012, that request changed to one for a hymn about joy and hope, especially using the Matthew 6:25-34 passage on the lilies of the field, which was one of the texts read at Trudy's funeral.

February 28, 2012
8.6.8.6 iambic
Based on Psalm 42 and Matthew 6:25-34
Commissioned by Jon Strommen Campbell in memory of his mother, Trudy H. Enstad Campbell, 1946–2012

Beyond the Mind's Imagining
Craig Dobbins of Sewickley Presbyterian Church in Sewickley, Pennsylvania, contacted me to write a text for the 175th anniversary of the church, twelve miles from Pittsburgh on the Ohio River. The name Sewickley derives from a Native American word, perhaps from the Early Mound Builders, meaning "sweet water," possibly referring to the multitude of sugar maples in the area. The text is built on the congregation's selected scripture passage for the anniversary, Ephesians 3:20-21: "Now to him who by the power at work within us is able to accomplish abundantly more than all we can ask or imagine, to him be glory in the church and in Christ Jesus to all generations, forever and ever. Amen."

August 9, 2013
8.6.8.6.8.6 iambic
Based on Ephesians 3:20-21 and the congregation's mission statement

Blessed One, Paragon

For a number of years, I have had an increasing desire to reclaim some of my tradition's lost reverence for Mary, mother of our Lord. I dipped my toe in the water with one stanza in the Christmas hymn "O Infinite Greatness, O Limitless Good," and having encountered the beautiful Scottish melody "Ca' the Yowes," decided to attempt a text wedded to this tune. Reading many of the Eastern early church writers, I found a trove of rich and beautiful images of Mary. John of Damascus wrote that "the name of the Mother of God contains all the history of the divine economy in this world"; Jacob of Serugh wrote that Mary was "shining forth with God," and St. Ephrem the Syrian, in a nativity hymn, compared Mary to the burning bush: "In the fire, Moses saw thy beauty in Shadow, O Daughter of David, in whose bosom dwelt the Flame, and thou wast not consumed, O Mother of God, and full of grace."

December 17, 2013
3.3.7.7.5 trochaic
Drawing from Irenaeus of Lyon, John of Damascus, Ephrem the Syrian, Cyril of Alexandria, Jacob of Serugh, and Luke 2
Written specifically for the Scottish folk tune CA' THE YOWES

Come, O Spirit, Come to Us (Veni Sancte Spiritus)

The Pentecost sequence Veni Sancte Spiritus, sometimes called the "Golden Sequence," has been attributed to Pope Innocent III (thirteenth century.). Dr. Samuel Torvend lamented that many translations of the Latin do not preserve the structure, the rhyme, and the repeated verbs, and so I tried a translation for him.

June 5, 2013
7.7.7 trochaic
Exact source unknown, attributed to Innocent III
For my dear friend Samuel Torvend

God Has Told Us, God Has Taught Us

Scott Hyslop, cantor at St. Lorenz Lutheran Church, Frankenmuth, Michigan, and spouse, Dora, requested a hymn text for the confirmation of their son, Nicholas, on Palm/Passion Sunday, March 20, 2016. They asked that the text reflect Micah 6:8 and Nicholas's confirmation text, Romans 8:38–39, and I wove in the phrase "love and trust in God" from the explanation of the Ten Commandments in Luther's Small Catechism.

February 18, 2016
8.7.8.7.7.7 trochaic
Based on Micah 6:8 and Romans 8:38–39

God, Who Set the Spheres in Motion

St. John's Episcopal Church, Lafayette Square, Washington, DC, commissioned a text to celebrate their bicentennial in 2016. Composer William Bradley Roberts was commissioned to write the tune. They asked for a text for any season, which could be a gift to the greater church. The text from the proper preface for the dead, *"vita mutatur non tollitur"*—"life is changed, not taken away"—has greatly shaped my beliefs since I first read it on a card over forty years ago, and I felt that I should write a text for All Saints and funerals, though an unlikely theme for an anniversary celebration, using this text as an anchor. Also embedded in the text are another phrase from the Book of Common Prayer: "Even at the grave we make our song: Alleluia," and a passage from the Apostolic Constitutions (c. 400 CE): "in the funerals of the departed, accompany them with singing" (AC 6:XXX). Dr. Benjamin Hutto, one of the original instigators of the commission, died on September 29, 2015, just a week before the text was completed.

October 6, 2015
8.7.8.7.D trochaic
Drawn from Ecclesiastes 1:7; 3:1; proper preface for the dead; Book of Common Prayer: Burial Rite II; and the Mourner's *Kaddish*

Great God, Whose Story

The 2014 National Lutheran-Anglican Worship Conference in Edmonton, Alberta, chose for its theme "Weaving Strands: Liturgy for Living." Drawing on John August Swanson's 2007 serigraph "The Procession" and his explanation that "We, in our communities of faith, are a procession of stories, stories both unique and shared," this hymn of interwoven stories took shape.

June 10, 2013
8.8.8.8.8.8 iambic
Images drawn from Psalm 139:13, 15; Ecclesiastes 4:12

Holy Woman, Graceful Giver

This hymn text is a variant on one that appears in volume 1 of this series, *O Blessed Spring.* There the hymn is based on the account of the unnamed woman with the jar of ointment who appears in Mark 14. The parallel telling in John 12 names the woman as Mary of Bethany; other details also vary between the gospels. The two hymn versions reflect these differences. Both are included in this volume for ease of reference.

April 28, 2016
8.8.7.8.8.7 trochaic
Based on John 12:1-8

How Beautiful, O God, How Good

Lutheran Social Service of Minnesota CEO Jodie Harpstead contacted both David and me about writing a hymn for the celebration of 150 years of Lutheran Social Service in Minnesota. LSS specifically requested that the text avoid the use of adjectives as nouns (e.g., *disabled, needy*), which then define and limit people to their current condition. The staff of LSS also asked for a text that celebrates God's abundance, as signified by the story of the multiplication of loaves and fishes. The phrase "God's desire pursues us" is from Abraham Heschel's *The Prophets.*

March 12, 2015
8.7.8.7.8.8 iambic
Based on Genesis 1; Psalm 133; Matthew 5; John 6; and Abraham
Heschel's *The Prophets*

How Lovely Is Your Dwelling Place
Trinity English Lutheran Church in Fort Wayne, Indiana, completed a
renovation for accessibility, also including a conversion to geothermal heat-
ing and cooling in 2009, and commissioned a text for the dedication of the
renovated space, wanting to focus on welcome and mission of all people,
and so I centered the text on Psalm 84.

September 13, 2009
8.8.8.8 (long meter)
Based on Psalm 84

How Shall We See the Realm of God?
As a hymn writer, I try to fill gaps in the existing hymnody and provide
hymn texts for lectionary readings for which not many or no hymns exist.
After a very fine sermon by the Reverend Arthur Halbardier on Matthew
13 at Mount Olive Lutheran Church in 2014, I was inspired to write this
text on all the images of the realm of God in Proper 12, Year of Matthew
(A).

8.8.8.8.8.8 with 8.8 iambic (long meter doubled)
Inspired by a sermon by the Reverend Arthur Halbardier on Matthew 13
Additional possible tune: O GROSSER GOTT

How Wondrous Is Your Steadfast Love
As a gift for the wedding of Sean Horner and Samuel Torvend on August
3, 2014, at St. Paul's Episcopal Church, Seattle, Washington, David and I
wrote a hymn loosely based on the pericopes for that Sunday, Proper 13,
Year A.

July 22, 2014
8.8.8.8.8.8 iambic
Drawn from Psalms 17:7; 145:9, 16; Matthew 14:20; Acts 17:28

In Love God Imagined the Worlds to Light
Southport Presbyterian Church in Southport, North Carolina, commissioned this hymn, both text and tune, in memory of the Reverend Mary Alice Haynie, who died of cancer in 2012. They requested a text that portrays the presence of God, citing Psalm 73, from which I chose the phrase "you hold my right hand" (v. 23) and "My flesh and my heart may fail, but God is the strength of my heart" (v. 26), as well as the words from the congregational mission statement: "Deeper in truth, Broader in service . . . Stronger in unity."

May 9, 2015
10.8.10.8. 6.5.8 dactylic, var.
Based on Psalms 73:23-26 and 139, the congregational mission statement, and the Reverend Mary Alice Haynie: "Words matter . . . listen to the people pray."

Like Morning Dew Afresh upon the Mount
Elaine and Arthur Halbardier commissioned this hymn for the fiftieth wedding anniversary of their dear friends Michael and Mary Alice Long of St. Louis, Missouri, but they desired a text that could be for the broader church as well. Each stanza has fifty syllables, five lines of ten, and the opening letter of each stanza spells out L-o-n-g. The Longs are also hidden in the text in the words "longing" and "belonging" (st. 2), as well as references to singing in choir and enjoying feasting with dear friends.

April 5, 2011
10.10.10.10.10 iambic
Based on Isaiah 25:6, 9; Psalm 133; Isaiah 55:1-2; and Ecclesiasticus 6:14; 9:19

No Word Expresses You, O God

Bethlehem Lutheran Church in Cherokee, Iowa, commissioned this text for the fiftieth anniversary of their congregation in the hills of west-central Iowa. The opening lines are based on the Anaphora of St. John Chrysostom: "For no word can express you, O God, no mind understand you, no eyes behold you, no intelligence grasp you—you who have existed from all eternity and have always been the same." I used images referring to the rich farmlands surrounding the town, as well as the word *gold* to point to the anniversary at hand. I admit to seeing how many appropriate rhetorical devices I could use during the crafting of the text, probably the most obvious of which is anaphora, or repeated use of the same words in the beginning of subsequent lines, given the model of Chrysostom's words.

May 28, 2014
8.6.8.6.8.8 iambic
Based on Genesis 1; Philippians 2:1–12; and
the Eucharistic Prayer of St. John Chrysostom (sts. 1, 5)

O Christ, unto Your Cross We Raise

Lutheran Church of the Cross in Port Charlotte, Florida, persisted through many legal roadblocks and finally succeeded in erecting a tall cross monument near their church, visible for miles around. This text and tune were commissioned by the congregation for the dedication of that monument and how it represents their mission. I wove together repeated uses of the word *lift*, drawing from John 12:32: "If I be lifted up, I will draw all to me"; 1 Timothy 2:8: "I desire, then, that in every place the people should pray, lifting up holy hands without anger or argument," and the Sursum corda, "Lift up your hearts," from the eucharistic liturgy.

November 25, 2013
8.8.8.8.8.8 iambic
Based on Mark 8:4; John 12:32, 34; 1 Timothy 2:8;
and from the communion liturgy Sursum corda ("Lift up your hearts")

O God, Great Love, Most Radiant, Bright

Cantor Scott Hyslop requested a hymn text that might be appropriate for Christmas, Pentecost, Trinity, or a day celebrating God as Creator. He asked for four stanzas that might be suitable to be set as a round, so I set the words in the simple long meter (four iambic lines of eight syllables) and based the text on these trinitarian images:

Richard of St. Victor (d. 1173):
For God to be truth, God had to be one;
for God to be love, God had to be two;
for God to be joy, God had to be three. (*The Trinity, Book III*)

and Hildegard von Bingen (1098–1179):
The Father is brightness
and this brightness has a flashing-forth
and in this flashing-forth is fire
and these three are one. (*Scivias*)

May 14, 2015
8.8.8.8 iambic (long meter)

O God of Fire, O Word of Flame

Michael Bauer of St. John's Lutheran Church in Bennington, Nebraska, contacted me to request a Pentecost hymn that could be sung to an existing tune, so I chose to work in long meter (four lines of eight iambic syllables). I worked from Acts 2 along with a story from the Desert Fathers: "Abba Lot came to Abba Joseph and said, according as I am able, I keep my little rule, and my little fast, my meditation, prayer and contemplative silence, and according as I am able, I strive to cleanse my heart of thoughts: now what more should I do? The elder rose up and stretched out his hands to heaven, and his fingertips became like ten lamps of fire. He said: Why not become fire?"

May 7, 2011
8.8.8.8 iambic (long meter)
Based on Acts 2 and the Desert Fathers
Suggested tunes:
BEATUS VIR, CONDITOR ALME SIDERUM, DEO GRATIAS, PUER NOBIS

O God of Wonders

For its 100th anniversary, Minnehaha Academy of Minneapolis commissioned both text and tune for a new school hymn to augment its march-like 1917 school hymn. David Cherwien was to write not only a tune and four-part vocal setting but also settings for choir, band, and orchestra. The tune was to be singable for grades K–12. The refrain begins with the letters MA for Minnehaha Academy, and ends with the letters MN for Minnesota, and includes references to the school's setting, education, the arts, science, math, and sports. The hymn was also used in 2014 for the October 10, 2014, inauguration of Paula J. Carlson as president of Luther College, Decorah, Iowa.

July 20, 2012
10.10.10.10 with refrain 10.10 iambic

O Heart of God

Each February, Plymouth Congregational Church in Wichita, Kansas, hosts an event combining theology and the arts called Word and Note. Howard Webb, choirmaster of the church, contacted both David and me to request a new hymn for the 2016 event. Pastor Don Olsen suggested a hymn incorporating a theme of relationship: between God and creation, God and human, human with creation, humans with each other. It is based on Pierre Teilhard de Chardin's statement, "By means of all created things, without exception, the divine assails us, penetrates us, and moulds us. We imagined [the Divine] as distant and inaccessible, whereas in fact we live steeped in its burning layers. In eo vivimus" (*The Divine Milieu*, p. 112), as well as Bohm's theory and the theory of quantum entanglement.

January 9, 2016
11.10.11.10.10.10 iambic
Based on Psalm 139; John 15; Acts 17:28; Ephesians 2:21-22; and Revelation 21, among others

O Infinite Greatness, O Limitless Good

It is not very often that individuals commission a hymn text, but in the winter of 2012, Mark, Jessinia, and Kaiya Ruff of Mount Olive Lutheran Church, Minneapolis, requested a Christmas text to be set as a choral anthem in honor of Lisa Ruff, wife and mother, on the occasion of Mark and Lisa's wedding anniversary. It has four stanzas, four, the number of the earth, to depict the Incarnation. "Infinite Greatness" is taken from James of Sarugh's (d. 521) *Hymn to Mary the Virgin* in which he wrote, "Blessed is she: her narrow womb enclosed the infinite Greatness which even the heavens are too small to contain." "This luminous feast" is from a prayer in a fifth-century Syriac Christmas liturgy. Stanza two is my first attempt to write a text about Mary, drawing from Proverbs 31 and, again, James of Sarugh ("Blessed is she: she fed at her breast him who stirs up the waves of the sea"). The Ruff family is very active with Common Hope in Guatemala, and that is woven into the text of stanza 3. A paraphrase of Meister Eckhardt gives the key to the final stanza: God is always needing to be born.

December 9, 2012
For the Feast of the Nativity of Our Lord
11.11.11.11.3 dactylic
Based on Proverbs 8; 31; Luke 2; John 1

O Not to Us

In 2012 Cantor Scott Hyslop celebrated twenty-five years of music ministry and commissioned a hymn text based on Psalm 115, one of the Hallel psalms sung at Passover, to which I added phrases from Psalms 108 and 135.

March 20, 2012
8.6.8.6 iambic
Based on Psalms 95; 108; and 115

Shall I Not Praise God with Singing (Sollt ich meinem Gott nicht singen)
In 2014 Scott Hyslop of Frankenmuth, Michigan, gave me a challenging assignment: write a new translation of Paul Gerhardt's twelve-stanza hymn, "Sollt ich meinem Gott nicht singen." Translation is a much different task from newly composing a text, because, to be fair, one has to honor the style, form, and conventions of the original writer. So I left many phrases and words in this text that I myself would not write. It was especially hard for me to leave the male pronouns for God, the language of substitutionary sacrifice, and passages alluding to an angry God, but leave them I did. It is, after all, seventeenth-century Paul Gerhardt's hymn, not mine.

July 10, 2014
Translated from Paul Gerhardt's "Sollt ich meinem Gott nicht singen" 1659
8.7.8.7.8.7.7.8.7.7 trochaic

Sing, Oh, Sing, the Threefold God
For the 125th anniversary of the congregation, Grace Lutheran Church in Lincoln, Nebraska, commissioned a joyful Trinitarian hymn based on its anniversary theme: "Making Christ known to all through grace." The text has five stanzas of twenty-one syllables, thus the odd iamb in the second line. Parts of the text are based on a prayer by Richard Rohr, OFM: "God for us, we call you Father. God alongside us, we call you Jesus. God within us, we call you Holy Spirit," and on Luther's Small Catechism.

April 23, 2015
7.7.7.4 trochaic

Spirit of God, Resound in Us

When the vestry at Mount Olive Lutheran Church, Minneapolis, realized that in September 2016 David Cherwien would be marking thirty-five years of full-time music ministry to the Lutheran church, they commissioned me to write a hymn text to commemorate the event. Composer William Beckstrand, who had served Mount Olive as interim cantor in 2013 while David was on sabbatical, was commissioned to write a tune and setting for the text. Usually I begin with a scripture passage, but in this unusual instance, I drew on all that I know about the inherent power of music to inspire, reveal, and shape us to be beautiful, creative, open, and loving images of God. The closing "alleluia" was inspired by the Orthodox kontakion refrain.

August 1, 2016
8.8.8.8.4 opening dactyl followed by iambs, with closing dactyl
Commissioned by Mount Olive Lutheran Church to celebrate the thirty-five years of full-time music ministry of Cantor David Cherwien

What Joyous Song Unfolding

When the pan-Lutheran Association of Lutheran Church Musicians (ALCM) celebrated twenty-five years of existence in 2011, plans were made for broad participation in a hymn festival designed and distributed nationally. This hymn was commissioned as a part of the celebration and was included in the hymn festival, preceded by a reflection written by Dr. Paul Westermeyer. I wrote the text to fit the Finnish melody NOORMARKKU, which was not included in recent Lutheran worship resources, and thus I feared would be lost.

September 11, 2011
7.6.7.6.D iambic
Tune: NOORMARKKU

Who Is This, That Winds Obey Him

For the 2015 meeting of the Institute of Liturgical Studies at Valparaiso University, "Sing a New Song: The Cosmos in Praise and Lament," composer Timothy Strand and I were commissioned to write a hymn based on the pericopes for Proper 12 in the Year of Mark (lectionary year B), the gospel reading of which is Jesus' calming of the storm. The funds for the commission were donated by Bridget Jensen of Houston, Texas, in honor of her companion, Pastor Arthur Preisinger, for whom the tune is named

November 19, 2014
8.7.8.7.8.7.8.7 trochaic
Based on Job 38:1-11; Psalm 107:1-3, 23-32; Mark 4:35-41; 2 Corinthians 6:1-13 (Pericopes for year B, Proper 12)

KEY WORD AND THEMATIC INDEX

*For convenience, this index includes hymns from volume 1 (O Blessed Spring),
volume 2 (Come, Beloved of the Maker), and this volume 3 (Peace, Be Still).
They are marked with volume numbers.*

SCRIPTURE REFERENCES

For convenience, this index includes hymns from volume 1 (O Blessed Spring),
volume 2 (Come, Beloved of the Maker), and this volume 3 (Peace, Be Still).
They are marked with volume numbers.

Genesis
1	*We sing the one God*	*1*
12:2	*A ram's horn blasting barren hills*	*1*
15:5	*We sing the one God*	*1*
15:12	*O sacred River*	*1*
15–18	*Exalted be your name*	*2*

Exodus
3	*In the desert, on God's mountain*	*1*
3:5	*In sacred manner*	*1*
13:21-22	*We sing the one God*	*1*
15–18	*Exalted be your name*	*2*
17:1-7	*O God, with hope I enter in*	*2*

Numbers
24:17	*As the dark awaits the dawn*	*1*

Deuteronomy
5:22-23	*O sacred river*	*1*

1 Samuel
16:15	*A ram's horn blasting barren hills*	*1*

1 Kings
8:22-30	*Most High, O holy God*	*2*

2 Kings
19:30	*For such a time as this*	*2*

2 Chronicles
5:12-13	*A ram's horn blasting barren hills*	*1*

Ezra
3	*All-embracing God*	*3*

Esther
4:14	*For such a time as this*	*2*

Job
12:7	*In sacred manner*	*1*
38:1-11	*Who is this, that winds obey him*	*3*
38:7	*A ram's horn blasting barren hills*	*1*
38:19	*From the dwelling place of light*	*2*

28:1-10	*In the fair morning*	1

Mark

1:13-15	*As your Spirit in the desert*	3
4:35-41	*Who is this, that winds obey him*	3
8:4	*O Christ, unto your cross we raise*	3
14:3-9	*Holy woman, graceful giver (Mark 14)*	1
14:34	*In deepest night*	1

Luke

1:26-38	*Blessed One, Paragon*	3
	Signs and wonders lead the dancing	2
2	*O Infinite Greatness, O Limitless Good*	3
4:18	*By grace God calls us into life*	2
14:12-13, 24	*O sacred River*	1
19:1-10	*Most High, O holy God*	2
24:1-7	*In the fair morning*	1
24:13-35	*Day of arising*	1
24:13-43	*Behold, unveiled the vesper skies*	2
24:28-35	*Blessing be and glory*	1

John

1	*O Infinite Greatness, O Limitless Good*	3
	Once grace and love did come to dwell	2
6	*Abide in us, O Bread of Life*	3
	How beautiful, O God, how good	3
10:10	*New things, O God*	2
11:35	*In deepest night*	1
12:1-8	*Holy woman, graceful giver (John 12)*	3
12:24	*Rich in promise*	1
12:32, 34	*O Christ, unto your cross we raise*	3
13:13-17, 20	*New things, O God*	2
15	*Beloved and most loving Source*	2
15:5	*O blessed spring*	1
20:19-31	*Rise, O church, like Christ arisen*	1
21:9-14	*Blessing be and glory*	1

Acts

2	*O God of Fire, O Word of Flame*	3
2:1-4	*We sing the one God*	1
14:3	*Signs and wonders lead the dancing*	2
17:28	*How wondrous is your steadfast love*	3
	O Fire of Love	2

Romans
  4:13-25   *As the showers that water the earth* 2
  6:3-9   *Christ is the life*   1
  6:11, 13   *The journey was chosen*   1
  8:38-39   *God has told us, God has taught us* 3
  10:13-17   *New things, O God* 2
  12   *Beyond the singing starlight* 2
  14:8   *Christ is the life*   1

1 Corinthians
  2   *O Fire of Love* 2
  15:49   *Come, beloved of the Maker* 2

2 Corinthians
  3:12   *Signs and wonders lead the dancing* 2
  5   *All-embracing God*   3

Galatians
  3:27   *Field of stars, awash in splendor* 2

Ephesians
  2:19-22   *Most High, O holy God* 2
  3:20-21   *Beyond the mind's imagining*   3

Philippians
  2   *Once grace and love did come to dwell* 2
  2:1-12   *No word expresses you O God*   3
  2:5   *O God of Wonders*   3
  4   *You fill all creation* 2
  4:8   *O God of Wonders*   3

Colossians
  1:15   *Come, beloved of the Maker* 2
  1:15-18   *O Fire of Love* 2
  1:15-20   *Christ, burning Wisdom* 1
              Image of the unseen God 2
  3:12-16   *Beloved, God's chosen* 1

1 Timothy
  2:8   *O Christ, unto your cross we raise* 3

Hebrews
  1:3   *As the dark awaits the dawn* 1

CHURCH YEAR INDEX

For convenience, this index includes hymns from volume 1 (O Blessed Spring),
volume 2 (Come, Beloved of the Maker), and this volume 3 (Peace, Be Still).
They are marked with volume numbers.

Signs and wonders, lead the dancing   2
Up from the earth in bright array   2

Easter 2 B (Ps)
Like morning dew afresh   3

Pentecost ABC
Come, O Spirit, come to us   3
O God of Fire, O Word of Flame   3
Spirit of God, resound in us   3

Holy Trinity ABC
By grace God calls us into life   2
Come, let us sing   2
No word expresses you, O God   3
O God, Great Love   3
Sing, oh, sing, the threefold God   3
When out of darkness   2

Lectionary 10 / Proper 5 A
As the showers that water the earth   2

Lectionary 17 / Proper 12 A
O Christ, unto your cross   3
God has told us, God has taught us   3

Lectionary 17 / Proper 12 B
Who is this, that winds obey him   3

Lectionary 22 / Proper 17 A
How shall we see the realm of God?   3

Lectionary 22–26 B / Propers 17–21 B
Abide in us, O Bread of Life   3
How beautiful, O God, how good

Lectionary 27 / Proper 22 A
O Christ, unto your cross we raise   3

Lectionary 28 / Proper 23 C
O Christ, unto your cross we raise   3

Mary, Mother of Our Lord
Blessed One, Paragon   3

Holy Cross Day
Bright joining   1
O Christ, unto your cross we raise   3

Lectionary 30 / Proper 25 C
How lovely is your dwelling place   3

All Saints Day
Come, new heaven, new earth descending   2
God, who set the spheres in motion   3

Christ the King
Before the Ancient One, Christ stands   2
Come, beloved of the Maker   2
Come, new heaven, new earth descending   2
Image of the unseen God   2

METRICAL AND TUNE NAME INDEX

METER	HYMN NAME	TUNE NAME
LM	How lovely is your dwelling place	Trinity English
LM	O God, great Love, most radiant, bright	Gladstone
LM	O God of Fire, O Word of Flame	Conditor alme siderum
LMD	How shall we see the realm of God?	In Parables
3.3.7.7.5	Blessed One, Paragon	Ca' the yowes
5.5.9.5.5.9	All-embracing God	Virginia Square
7.6.7.6.D	What joyous song unfolding	Noormarkku
7.7.7	Come, O Spirit, come to us	Veni Sancte Spiritus
7.7.7.4	Sing, oh, sing, the threefold God	Grace Unending
8.6.8.6	Abide in us, O Bread of Life	Feast of Life
8.6.8.6	Behold the lilies of the field	Trudy
8.6.8.6	O not to us	Not to Us
8.6.8.6.8.6	Beyond the mind's imagining	Sewickley
8.6.8.6.8.8	No word expresses you, O God	Bethlehem, Cherokee
8.7.8.7 and refrain	As your Spirit in the desert	Roseville
8.7.8.7.D	God, who set the spheres in motion	Lafayette Square
8.7.8.7.D	Who is this, that winds obey him	Preisinger
8.7.8.7.7.7	God has told us, God has taught us	Písti, elpída, kai agápi
8.7.8.7.8.8	How beautiful, O God, how good	Norelius
8.7.8.7.8.7.7.8.7.7	Shall I not praise God with singing?	Sollt ich meinem Gott
8.8.7.8.8.7	Holy woman, graceful giver	Alabaster
8.8.8.8.4	Spirit of God, resound in us	Anno tringinta quinque
8.8.8.8.8.8	Great God, whose story	Edmonton New
8.8.8.8.8.8	How wondrous is your steadfast love	Seanuel
8.8.8.8.8.8	O Christ, unto your cross we raise	Port Charlotte
10.8.10.8.6.5.8	In love God imagined the worlds to light	Haynie
10.10.10.10 and refrain	O God of Wonders	Minnehaha New
10.10.10.10.10	Like morning dew afresh upon the mount	MM Long
11.10.11.10.10.10	O Heart of God	Plymouth
11.11.11.11.3	O Infinite Greatness, O Limitless Good	Marlis

COMPOSER INDEX

ABOUT THE AUTHOR

Susan Palo Cherwien was born in 1953 in Ashtabula, Ohio, where she was generously exposed to the music and poetry of the Christian tradition at Zion Evangelical Lutheran Church. She was especially influenced by her time in the children's choir, directed by Vicar Martin Lundi, who assigned her first solo—in Finnish. Susan began writing poetry in grade school and continued throughout her adolescent years and into her time at Wittenberg University, where she studied church music and vocal performance. In her junior year, she attended the Berliner Kirchenmusikschule, and then returned to Berlin to study voice from 1976 to 1981 after graduating from Wittenberg.

Not until 1987 did she begin to combine her passion for music, poetry, and spirituality in the composing of hymn texts. In 1993 Susan completed a master's degree in liberal studies at Mundelein College, Chicago, where she focused on spirituality, ritual, and the arts. She lives in St. Louis Park, Minnesota, with her spouse, David.